A DAIRYMAIDS FLORA

BY CHRIS HOWKINS

C. Howkins

PUBLISHED BY
CHRIS HOWKINS

WRITTEN AND ILLUSTRATED BY
Chris Howkins

COPYRIGHT
Chris Howkins 1994 ©

ISBN 0 9519348 5 6

PUBLISHED BY

Chris Howkins,
70, Grange Road,
New Haw,
Addlestone,
Surrey, KT15 3RH.

PRINTED BY

Ian Allan Printing,
Coombelands House,
Cooombelands Lane,
Addlestone,
Surrey, KT15 1HY.

CONTENTS

INTRODUCTION

THIS BOOK is for people who enjoy the countryside and in particular the flowers and trees, fields and farms. It is no ordinary Flora but concentrates upon some 60 plants, from a much longer list, which were useful to our ancestors in providing for their everyday needs in their dairying activities.

Our ancestors used some of the plants for sound practical reasons, like the trees with wood suited to serving as pails and stools, bowls and strainers. Some plants have sap that will curdle milk for making cheese while others have big leaves for wrapping butter. From another list come plants which are linked with ancient beliefs, most of which are pagan because the time scale for dairying stretches back some 6,000 years before Christ. Nevertheless, attention is drawn to some that were Christianised, particularly those used connected with the Midsummer celebrations that began on the Eve of the Feast of St.John the Baptist (June 23rd). This lost much of its importance after the Reformation.

The plants have been grouped according to their function so as to avoid repetition in explaining the reason for their usage. Plants in each section are then in alphabetical order of their standard English name. There is an index of both English and botanical names.

The more the plants were sought out and studied for this book the more important it became to understand more about the history of dairying itself. To present that adequately would take a very large volume so only a few of the aspects can be highlighted here, both from history and from the studies made on a present-day dairy farm. A small portion of the resulting material from that farm study is presented here to encourage further recording before this rapidly changing way of life has gone for good. There are a number of sites now being preserved as 'old cow pastures'.

They are rich in wild flowers but would that have been so in the days when they were managed for dairying? Some of the flowers being conserved would have pleased our ancestors while others they would perhaps have condemned. There is still a great deal of information to gather and conservation management to learn.

A book as small as this can be only an introduction to what is an extensive subject. The material has been collected over some fourteen years as part of a wider study of the plants used in Britain by our ancestors. Fresh material seems to arrive everyday but more is always welcome. Please write to the publisher's address.

ACKNOWLEDGEMENTS

A vast list of published materials has been consulted together with the collecting of information from original documents. To this has been added the learning of many individuals and organisations, to whom is extended a very sincere thank you. In particular, for checking and updating some of the material for this particular book thanks are due to the Ministry of Agriculture, the National Institute of Agricultural Botany, the Royal Horticultural Society, the Royal Pharmaceutical Society of Great Britain, Surrey County Library, and officers at Hampton Court Palace; to Mr A. Long of Vegetarian Economy and Green Agriculture, Mrs J. Roberts of the Milk Marketing Board; Mrs J. Leslie of the Surrey Flora Committee for help in locating some of the plants for the illustrations, Mrs D. Grimm for help in locating the wooden dairying artifacts illustrated and to Mr D. Hemsley for help in creating the finished book.

Mr and Mrs S. Pennington and all at Pondtail Farm deserve very warm thanks for their inspiration and generosity in allowing our study of their dairy farm and for sharing their knowledge and experience.

"He that will have
his farm full
must keep an old cock
and a young bull"

[proverb]

SETTING THE SCENE

Before delving into the ways plants have been put to use in dairying practices it is important to appreciate three main points which will have a bearing upon the content of the folowing pages.

Firstly, the time scale is so lengthy as to stretch back some 8,000 years and includes many cultures. For example many of our country 'superstitions' have their origins in Greek mythology, and while they survive in this superstitious way it is very difficult to give precise dates for the various uses and activities.

Secondly, cows were highly valued. In cultures like the Celtic they were the main unit of taxation. This worked well-enough in Ireland and those parts of Western England where the warming influence of the Atlantic kept frosts away, enabling pasturage throughout the year. In colder regions pigs replaced cows. Countless village histories begin with the entry from the Norman Doomsday Book of 1086 where the valuation is given in pigs. Of course these were not real live pigs but units of value. Nevertheless, the cow did not lose her worth in that she and her produce were taken into account when calculating a person's dues for the church tithe. This system of taxation lasted until recent times.

Thirdly, for most of the time span considered, dairying was only a seasonal activity. The cow, like the other animals, gave birth in the spring and produced milk from then, on through the summer, before gradually drying out. Changing this natural pattern took many generations of selective breeding before today's position was reached whereby a milk supply can be guaranteed for every day of the year.

IN EARLIER TIMES

Caveman worshipped the bull, hoping that, through the processes of sympathetic magic, he too might be as strong and powerful. The cave paintings of France and Spain are an inspirational testament to those times but the cow was not ignored.

It was in the Middle East, in Upper Arabia, where archaeological evidence suggests domestication of the wild auroch had begun by 6000 BC. Within another couple of thousand years the cattle were established farm animals. Milk must have been wonderful to those peoples- warm, creamy, sweet and nutritive - what a contrast to the polluted water, thick with sand, to be had from the water holes and rivers. No wonder the Promised Land was a land of milk and honey. When the Egyptians needed a living image for Hathor, their goddess of love and of women, they turned to the cow. Today the cow is still held sacred by some of the world's peoples whereas in Britain it is more likely to be used as a term of abuse.

In the Middle East man began selective breeding, as described in the Bible and the 'breeds' are shown in Egyptian tomb paintings. Other regions were slower to develop the practice, except that animals got smaller, suggesting the larger more unruly beasts were the first to be culled for meat. That was the case in Britain until the Beaker People started arriving (1900-450 BC) from the Celtic heartland of the Swiss Lake People. They brought with them a new type of cow, smaller and lighter with shorter horns that curved forwards, maintained for dairying. It is from the Celtic cow that most modern dairy breeds are believed to have descended. It was the Celtic Belgae peoples who really got on with developing cattle farming and had at least four 'breeds'. Among these was one that is thought to be the ancestor of today's Jersey cow and another probably led to the Ayrshire.

Through all this time there has been the need to get the most and the best from the cattle and if possible to improve upon it. That is still true today and the dairy industry, being such 'big business', can be full of science and technology. Nevertheless the cow is still a creature, not a machine, and needs careful nurturing and feeding if she is to give her best. Her whole existence still depends upon plants. Thus during the compilation of this Flora parallel studies were made of the setting, on a modern dairy farm.

FARMS AND CONSERVATION

To understand more fully the setting for the use of wild British plants in dairying it was decided to run another parallel study of a dairy farm. Such places in the South East had been closing down with increasing regularity. The Ministry of Agriculture gave statistics that revealed closures in their South Eastern Region to be sixteen in 1990 while in 1991 the number shot up to sixty one. That totals a vast acreage of countryside for which alternative uses will be sought and which will in turn change the countryside dramatically. Alarmingly, we have but few studies of the relationship between farming activities and the wildlife which we are trying to conserve. It's another one of those "soon it will be too late" stories. Attention has tended to focus upon the 'big issues' like saving the wetlands. The small farms of just a few acres grouped around a commuter village are likely to be smiled upon as a "valuable green oasis" rather than have their cycles of activities studied for their role in a balanced, healthy Britain. There is much clamour for returning to 'traditional' farming but there are few people left in some districts who know the finer details of how that worked. There are many local history enthusiasts recording the memories of older generations and the workers of the land need their special attention.

Through an understanding of how the land was farmed will come the ability to conserve desired wildlife and scenery. The attempts to encourage wild flowers back into the sides of fields and their headlands is proving successful but ironically some sites are colourful with the very plants that would, in former years, have been weeded out for fear of them poisoning stock, tainting the milk, etc. Some of the plants would not have with-stood grazing, as the cow can be quite destructive. She wraps her tongue round the fodder and wedges it against her hard upper palate ready to tear it off. Should it prove tough then the lower jaw is brought up smartly to chop through the stems. Obviously pasture plants need to be anchored with strong roots to withstand that and to have the ability to sprout again from the base. The water meadows are known to have fewer flowers than other pastures because when they get inundated during floods a fertilizing deposit is left behind that encourages strong grasses to outgrow the weaker herbs. On the other hand studies on the Outer Hebridean island of South Uist are showing that the glorious wild flower meadows there are dependent upon the traditional crofting practice of fertilizing the fields with seaweed to bind the sand together.

It is not just the flora that suffers. The decline of the Barn Owl has been shown to be due to a significant extent upon the loss of old farm buildings as nest sites. Modern dutch barns do not answer the birds' needs at all; nesting boxes could, theoretically, be included by the manufacturers. The Lapwing, as a breeding species, is declining in certain areas and for this the changes in crops are being studied. There is a change over from Spring Barley to Autumn Barley, which upsets the way the bird's breeding cycle has adapted over the

Barn
Owl

centuries to suit the timing of the cropping. Then there is the Partridge, which is known to spend all its life beside the field of its birth but take the field away and where does the Partridge go? Thus the whole pattern of the land and its usage needs to be understood if the conservation measures are to be successful in keeping that which is valued.

FINDING A TYPICAL FARM TO STUDY

Finding a typical English farm is like trying to find a typical English pub. They are all different! Ideally what was needed was one as traditional as possible in the 1990s and yet economically successful, stretching its potential to the limit of the EC regulations. To trace such a farm, contact was made with a supervisor of the National Milk Records for such a person visits and knows every dairy farm within their region. Thus we met Mrs Jenny Roberts whose area covers West Surrey, N.E. Hants and the whole of Berkshire - one person is able to cover such a vast area because so few dairy farms remain. Among those, we were astonished how few might meet our needs and when it was specified that the cows must be of a traditional brown-and-white breed, rather than the modern black-and-white jobs, faces fell. There were only two where the cows were still milked in their stalls rather than in a special milking parlour.

Thus on one of the coldest, greyest February Snowdrop days Mrs Roberts led the way through the lanes of N.W. Surrey, to meet Mr Sidney Pennington Snr, at Pondtail Farm. He agreed to the study of his farm and proved wonderfully supportive.

He is one of the country's top Ayrshire breeders; to walk into his cowshed is to walk under roof beams that are encrusted with awards, right up to Reserve Breed Champions and Supreme Breed Champions: three such awards from three different cows in 1993 from the top shows, including the South of England Dairy Event at Ardingly and the Surrey County Show (the largest single-day event of its kind in the country). At such shows he is the longest serving exhibitor.

Mr S. Pennington, Snr.

   The Ayrshire breed is of ancient origin having been
bred out of old Scottish breeds by the farmers of
Dumbarton, Renfrew and Ayrshire to exploit the demand
for dairy produce from the rapidly growing industrial
areas of Paisley, Greenock and Glasgow. The high milk
yield suggests breeding with Dutch cattle while the
richness probably derives from Channel Island breeds
and constitutional toughness from the ancient Longhorns.
A key figure in the evolution of this new breed was one
John Dunlop who brought in outside breeds to his farm at
Dunlop House (c.1760), so they were known at first as
'Dunlops'. None other than Robert Burns was given a pair
by Mrs Dunlop when he began his Ellisland Farm. It is
said the local farmers had a keen eye for a good woman
too and chose fat ones for wives because they could put
more weight on the cheese presses!

Why does Mr Pennington
   like Ayrshires?

"Oh they're an ideal
type of dairy cow:
consistent breeders,
consistent milk
producers and long
wearing; been with
them since the
mid-thirties."

Cows enter their cowshed in the same order every time;
an order predetermined by the primitive herd instinct
which controls what looks like a random collection of
cows in a field. They return to the same stall each time
too. Here they will be milked and, in the severest of
winter weather, here they will stay all day.

The feeding of the cow is adjusted to her needs as she progresses through her period of lactation. This is made all the easier by her returning to the same stall each time - her particular supplements are there ready to greet her. A contented cow relaxes and lets her milk flow easily. Nevertheless, this is a rare scene.

Our ancestors had to rely upon the natural pasturage
to provide all the nutrients needed and of course there
were, on occasions, deficiencies. During the 17th and
18th centuries nutritious fodder crops were introduced
and developed. Today the fodder is supplemented with
special food pellets to ensure there are no deficiencies.
These are loaded out of the bags into the food trolley
and dished out at each stall according to need. These
contain the products and
by-products of
Oilseeds,
Sugar,
Cereals,
Legumes,
Forage plants,
Oils and fats,
Vitamins A,D3,E,
Selenium,
Copper,
Magnesium.

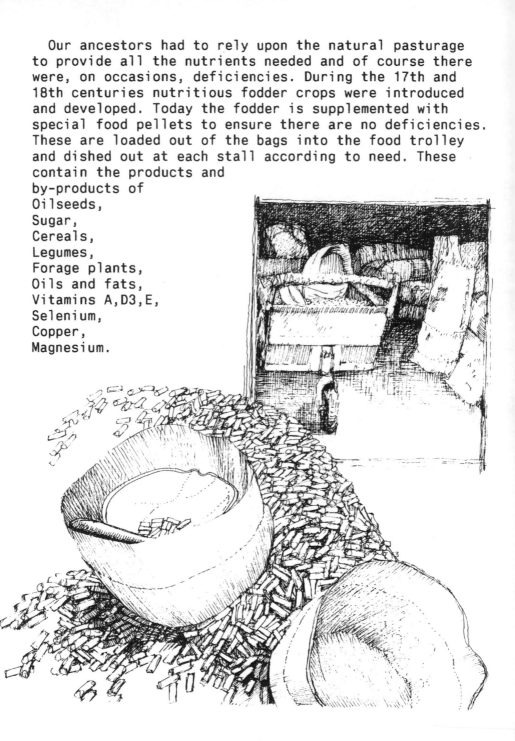

The Lane
To The Farm

It's all a far cry from when children were sent out to
collect flowering herbage to supplement the feed of the
family cow, and that was only in the 1950s for some.
There are 'modern' developments that are worth having.
It's neither desirable nor possible to ignore everything
modern; there must be compliance with EC standards and
regulations for one thing. The aim at Pondtail Farm is
to produce the best, without resorting to cruel methods,
and the tried and trusted means do bring results; when
the Penningtons first arrived, back in 1943, the farm
was only 106 acres and was not capable of keeping 23
cows through the winter. Now it has grown to 264 acres
(16 acres were lost to the construction of the M25) and
it supports 75 milking cows plus four bulls and the next
generations coming along - the calves, heifers and the
bull calves growing on for sale as fatstock. There are
also 60 sheep and 700 hens. The farm would, and has,
supported more but the dairy herd is restricted by the
EC regulations.

A well-fed cow produces most milk and of the highest quality so feeding is crucial. Although people like Mr Pennington only have to look at a cow's coat to see if she is in good condition, and it's the first thing he draws your attention to in the winter stalls, there is now a standardised system of ensuring good feeding. This is thanks to the Milk Recorders sent out by the Milk Marketing Board (reorganised into National Milk Records during the writing of this book). These recording visits are by agreement, not from being imposed by the government or EC.

Once a month these part-time workers visit each dairy farm to sample and analyse the milk from every single cow. They arrive before the afternoon milking session and set up a temporary recording station, which at Pondtail is a table-top board on an oil drum. Then the milking begins but instead of it being piped straight through to the cooler as per any other day it is collected in a sealed pail and brought to the recorder. She weighs it and takes a sample, labels it, and has it analysed into percentages of fat, protein, lactose etc. The pail is then taken away by the farm workers to the cooler or to be fed to the new calves.

Early next morning the recorder returns and does the same all over again. The two results for each cow are put together to get a 'whole milking'. The volume is ascertained from the weighing rather than measuring it in gallons or litres. (The spring balance is hung from a roof beam but was held for the benefit of illustration) Thus the fall in yield is monitored as the cow goes out of lactation and her feeding is adjusted accordingly. This gives the maximum return per investment. All the results are added to a profile that is kept of each cow. To complete this profile, details of the cow's breeding programme are added so that the farmer has standardised records authenticated by an outside agency. When it comes to trading he therefore knows exactly what he is buying and has the best chances of getting value for money. The consumer of the dairy produce has the same guarantee of quality and excellence.

Milk Recorder weighing milk.
The first ten daughters of
the bull 'Etherow Investment'
averaged 5,747 kg of milk per
lactation. Each lactation
averaged 305 days; can be
370 days.

To support the herd most of the feed is home-grown, making this farm unusual nowadays for being 'mixed'. There are thirty two acres of winter and spring barley, eight acres of winter oats and twenty four acres of forage maize which is turned into silage there in the field for direct feeding to the cattle. Primarily of course there is the grass, for grazing, for making eight hundred bales of hay and for two hundred bags of wrapped silage. In the days when most feed came from the old cow pastures some fifty species of flowers and grasses, at least, contributed to the daily pinta.

Fertility arises from that time-honoured practice of muck-spreading from a glorious great muck heap at the bottom of the yard. This is excellent for promoting lush fodder grasses and for soil conditioning. Many of the wild flowers get choked out by that lushness and so now conservationists realise that it is necessary to remove the mowings when the 'wild flower meadow' is cut so as not to enrich the soil too much. As the soil gets poorer so the plant diversity gets richer. It is a delicate balance where the traditional and the modern are incompatible. At Pondtail the muck-spreading is a winter activity, taking place in January if the weather permits. Looking at the heap Mr Pennington commented,

"You feed the land and the land will feed you.
Starve the land and you'll starve too."

People like Mr. Pennington hold in their heads many generations of wisdom. They not only know their animals and their farming practices but they have an intimate knowledge of their own acres - the variations in the soil and the micro-climate and which plants do best on which particular sites. This has not been superseded by modern science and technology. Building design, for example, was changed in the computer age with resulting illness in cows and pigs. Detailed studies followed. Only then was it realised that the old vernacular designs had evolved proportions that caused the air in the sheds to circulate in a healthy way. Modern designs dropped cold germ-laden air back round the stock.

Mr David Shaw

At Pondtail, stock is housed in vernacular buildings by what are largely traditional practices. These were learnt by Mr Pennington from his father and are being passed on to both his son, who works his own farm in conjunction with him, and to the cowman, Mr David Shaw. This is unusual nowadays when sons rarely follow fathers and young prospective farmers tend to go to Agricultural Colleges for their grounding.

THE ANNUAL CYCLE

The annual cycle of tasks varies from farm to farm and whether the season is 'early' or 'late' which in turn depends upon the weather. Into this cycle the species of the flora have to fit their own cycles - to shed seed before harvest time or quickly afterwards etc. Below is an outline of Pondtail's year which is more complicated than most because of it being a 'mixed' farm.

JANUARY

This is the main lambing time which began in December and will run on into February. Fencing began last month too and that continues. Weather permitting it is muck-spreading time, supplemented with sewage sludge.

FEBRUARY

The lambing season ends and so does the fencing. As soon after the 20th as possible the Spring Barley is sown and fertilized.

MARCH

Out comes the tractor to plough the fields intended for Maize and the Winter Barley has to be fertilized.

APRIL

Fertlizing the Barley is completed and if possible an early start can be made on the 'May' activities.

MAY

The sheep need shearing; the silage has to be cut and made; the Maize has to be sown; both the Spring and Winter Barley need spraying against noxious weeds like the poisonous Nightshades and against fungi that would be toxic if ingested.

JUNE

June is hay-making time: one of the most enduring traditions and one where science still can't overcome bad weather!

JULY

Rather like May, this is a busy month. The sheep need dipping; the second crop of silage should be ready for cutting; the Winter Barley is ripening ready for harvesting; the summer growth of the hedges is in need of trimming back.

26

AUGUST

Hedge trimming is completed; the Spring Barley is now ready for harvesting and it is time to let the ram have his way with the ewes.

SEPTEMBER

Ploughing begins again for the next crop of Winter Barley - the fields must be harrowed down ready to take the seed from the 20th onwards. By this time the Maize should be ready for harvesting.

OCTOBER

Both the Barley and the Maize harvests should come to an end and ditching begins.

NOVEMBER

It is the main time for the hedging and ditching; it's a long way around every field boundary on the farm but without it the winter rains will fill the ditches and flood the fields, the wind and snow will break gaps in the hedges and the livestock will wander. Having bulls on the farm makes this especially important.

DECEMBER

It's lambing time again and all the fencing needs checking and repairing if necessary.

MILK STIMULANTS

Our ancestors soon realised that cows produced the best milk after feeding in flowery pastures. The variety of the plants yielded a range of essential minerals and vitamins that improved health and therefore lactation. These wild flowers included some which stimulate the mammary glands into producing more milk than would otherwise be the case. These are known technically as galactogogues, from 'gala', the Greek for milk (hence the genus Galega and Polygala below). They were difficult to identify as any improvement in the diet was likely to improve the milk yield and disguise the true effect of the herbs. A few of these are described below:

ANISE (Pimpinella anisum) is a hardy annual thought to have come originally from Greece. Its very distinctive flavour soon brought it into cultivation and was being grown in Egypt by 1500 BC. It was popular with the Greeks and Romans too, both in food and drink but also in medicine, so that by the 1st century AD Pliny the Elder was listing over sixty remedies centred on anise. Its spread throughout Europe was due in no small part to Charlemagne's edict that all the herbs grown at the St.Gall monastery in Switzerland should be grown henceforth on his royal estates.

Anise (aniseed) was a very popular flavouring but does not do well in our climate. Consequently large amounts had to be imported and thereby attracted the attention of Edward I's ministers who, by 1305, had included it among the imported drugs due for taxation if they crossed London Bridge. This raised prices, making it unlikely that Anise was used for cattle but it also turned attention to cheap alternatives, such as Burnet Saxifrage and Fennel. Both of these herbs are galactogogues.

Anise
for the famous aniseed.

FENNEL (Foeniculum vulgare) is a grand architectural plant for the garden. It is believed to have been a Roman introduction from the Mediterranean; the earliest archaeological record in Britain is from a Roman site. It has since escaped from cultivation but in the wild is surprisingly scarce, considering how tough and persistent are the self-sown seedlings in gardens. In the wild it tends to be a coastal plant.

History implies it must have been much commoner in the past as it was grown widely, for so many purposes: as a pot herb, flavouring, fodder, dietary aid, cosmetic, fumigant, strewing herb, flea repellent, plus a wide range of uses in rites and rituals.

The Greeks grew it in pots for use in the eight-day celebration of Adonis (one of their vegetation deities) and this use alone took it to Alexandria, Assyria, Cyprus, Egypt, Judea, Persia and all over Greece. It became a Greek symbol of success, called Marathon, after their victory over the Persians at the city of that name in 490 BC. The Roman soldiers and sportsmen adopted it and spread its cultivation wider. It became highly valued for culinary and medicinal purposes but it never lost its spiritual significance: it became one of the nine sacred herbs of the Saxons, continued as a deterrent to evil in the Midsummer celebrations until very recently and is still viewed with some respect, as in such gardening lore as "Sow fennel, sow trouble."

The generic name, Foeniculum, comes from the Greek meaning 'little hay' and indeed the foliage does shrivel up to leave very little. Nevertheless, it was a valued food additive for man and beast, stimulating the appetite with its flavour and calming the digestive system with volatile oils (primarily fenchone and athenole). These actions improved lactation and promoted Fennel as a galactogogue. Similarly, it has been an important ingredient in babies' gripe water. Like all good things it must be treated with respect; large doses cause disturbance to the nervous system.

Collecting Fennel seed.

This century children were still
sent out to collect wild herbs,
eg. Aldbourne, Wilts. in 1920's.

The Second World War caused more
collecting of medicines from the
wild.

GOAT'S RUE (Galega officinalis),
despite its rather off-putting name,
is a handsome wild flower that has
naturalised itself from cultivation.
It was introduced in 1568 and comes
from Southern Europe and Western Asia.
It makes a fine herbaceous garden plant,
being easy to grow, largely self-supporting,
and flowering from late summer into autumn
when most needed. Particularly noticeable
is the white form, so pure it almost glows
in the half-light of an autumn evening.

It was grown as a fodder crop and
soon proved itself to be a most
effective stimulant for both
humans and animals. There have
been claims of it increasing milk
yield by 50%. Nowadays it is of more
interest for containing the alkaloid
called galegine which is a hypoglycaemic
agent, used sometimes in the management
of late-onset diabetes mellitus. The
fresh juice will clot milk and so has
been used as a rennet in cheese-making.

BURNET SAXIFRAGE (Pimpinella saxifraga) is one of the later flowering umbellifers, prefering dry alkaline soils. It is an attractive perennial, with dainty clear white flowers but has not won favour among gardeners. It has been known widely as a galactagogue, said to be especially effective with cows, but it is difficult to imagine that it could ever have been collected in quantities sufficient to be of real value.

MILKWORT (Polygala vulgaris) says it all with its English and botanical name but it is the slenderest of flowers. It nestles low among the Downland grasses, attracting attention with its bright blooms of white, purple or pure blue. It is so frail that it is highly unlikely to have been gathered in quantities sufficient to aid a cow. It was prescribed for human patients though. Gerard tells us it was sold in Cheapside by the herb women who knew it as 'Hedge Hyssop'. They sold it to those who knew no better as Gratiola, the true Hedge Hyssop. (Gratiola officinalis) is a drastic cathartic and emetic, against dropsy, scrofula or problems with the liver or spleen. It shifted worms too. The action of Milkwort as a stimulant has not been proven. Another species, **BITTER MILKWORT** (Polygala amara) has also been recommended but is more valuable as a bitter tonic.

BUTTERCUPS (Ranunculus spp.) have an odd reputation in that it is said that they were rubbed into cows' udders to improve the milk. The oddness lies in that Buttercups contain toxins of the protoanemonine group which cause burning and blistering when rubbed into flesh. Desperate people did this to themselves before going begging, so as to open up sores the better to encourage sympathetic donations. If over-done this no doubt drove away potential donors for fear that the beggar had leprosy: formerly a familiar and much feared disease in Britain. Treating the tender udder of a cow in this way was likely to be curtailed by the swift action of a hoof! Nevertheless, rubbing Buttercups into udders has been known in Ireland until recent times and was supposed to drive evil spirits away from taking the milk. Maybe, just maybe, handfuls of Buttercups were just dusted over the udder to leave a bitter taste behind. This may have been enough to encourage the calf to wean and thereby leave more milk for man.

Of the many and varied Buttercups in Britain, one in particular certainly does not stimulate milk. It brings production to a halt. This is the rather tasty-sounding **CELERY-LEAVED BUTTERCUP** (Ranunculus sceleratus) which is thought to be the most toxic of the Buttercups. This is reflected better in names in other languages, such as the American 'Cursed Crowfoot' and the French 'Mort aux vaches' or 'Herbes sardonique'. It has a virulent blistering action on all livestock. Cattle can be at particular risk because the plant prefers to grow in wet places such as around the animals' watering places. There it can be found growing quite luxuriantly.

DANDELION (Taraxacum officinale) is one of the most wonderful of British herbs in the range of nutritional and medicinal values. A monograph on Dandelions would be a sizeable study. Some animals, like rabbits, seek it out and thrive on it. Others, like sheep and cows, are far less enthusiastic; perhaps their sense of taste is keener in the bitter range. Nevertheless, Dandelions have the reputation of increasing a cow's milk yield.

Cellery-leaved Buttercup.

STINGING NETTLE (Urtica dioica) was the most celebrated of the dairying galactogogues. Today it is much maligned as a pernicious weed but it has been a valued source of textile fibre, dye, medicine and food, also flavouring for beer and tea; so much so that it was a marketable crop, recorded in medieval accounts. It must have been so common around the farms and villages because it loves the nitrate-rich soils associated with man's activities. Its defensive stings and the absence of herbicides were also to its advantage. It became an important crop in countries like Scotland, Denmark and Norway and is still used for medicines and as a source of chlorophyll.

Although it had at least four dozen specific uses, in the context of this study, it was its value as a fodder plant that was appreciated and exploited. This was especially so in countries like Sweden and Russia with their short growing seasons. Nettles are not even a crop that needs ripening in prolonged sunshine. It has been said that the Nettles could be cut five or six times each year but this may well be an commercial exaggeration as repeated cutting weakens and eventually kills even such a persistent plant as the Nettle. The Royal Horticultural Society has recommended three cuttings a year for three years to kill it.

Nettles were not fed fresh but cut and wilted first as only donkeys have the reputation for eating the herb fresh. It was also dried and mixed in with hay. Either way, milk yields increased. Part of this must be due to the general nutritive value of the good protein and fat content. In Germany, during the First World War, they not only exploited its fibre for making military uniforms in the absence of cotton supplies, but, also decreed that it should be harvested and dried for winter fodder.

WARNING : It is once again popular to recommend this plant for human consumption and it is indeed tasty and nutritive, but, like bananas, Stinging Nettles are a source of serotonin which has been implicated in

migraine and
certain heart
problems. They
should not be eaten
regularly in large
quantities as they
can then cause kidney
damage. The same is
true if eaten raw.
Yes, people used to eat
them raw! John Evelyn
recorded in his "Acetaria"
(1699) that they should be
"a little bruised."

Fresh interest in wild plants
as sources of raw materials has
led to many being investigated
by modern science to ascertain
the validity of their claims to
fame. Some of the galactogogues,
such as Borago officinalis, the
BORAGE, have been discredited.

MILK SUPPRESSANTS

Just as our ancestors learned which plants were the galactogogues to stimulate milk production so they also learned which plants would suppress or reduce the milk yield. There are at least three dozen species or groups of closely related species which act in this way, for which there is scientific documentation. In addition there are dozens more, regarded as suspect, or to be avoided according to country lore, for which further study is still awaited. A cow's milk yield drops as a symptom of it being unwell and so the milk suppressant plants are normally those which are described loosely as 'poisonous' plants. These are rarely constant but vary from plant to plant, site to site, year to year. Readers are alerted to the following as being some of the more notorious, leaving the morbid details in the veterinary and toxicology literature.

Our understanding of these risks should not be obscured by present-day images of cows fenced into rich green fields of grasses. These are comparatively recent scenes, following many centuries of 'rough' grazing with cattle feeding wherever there was food - through the woods, along lanes and hedgerows, out on stubble and so forth. Whenever grass was scarce and the cattle looked elsewhere for fodder then they were most at risk.

Woodlands may surprise some readers but these often had grazing rights in the past. There were glades of wild grasses (the original 'lawns') and other clearings like the grassy trackways called rides, from a Saxon word meaning to be clear of - hence our expression to be 'rid' of something. Many herbs, other than grasses, were within reach, whether for browsing or grazing.

The **OAK** (Quercus spp.) with its low spreading branches and richly hued new leaves tempts hungry herbivores and so the tree protects itself from browsing with high levels of tannins in the new growth. These substances have been known for centuries and exploited for tanning hides, where they bind the proteins together, but they do great harm to living cattle. This is made worse by them developing a craving for more, once they have started feeding on oak, something which is of serious economic importance in regions like the south western United States. It is also a risk in Britain but here more casualties occur in autumn when acorns are attractive. The tannins make the milk too bitter to use and then it dries up. Death can follow.

IVY (Hedera helix) in the woods is often said to be beneficial and has been fed deliberately to cattle as winter feed. However, our ancestors knew only to give small amounts. Too much will taint the milk and even more will dry up the cow, among other symptoms of poisoning. This is a relatively easy toxin to recognise as there is a strong smell of Ivy on the animal's breath.

BLUEBELL (Hyacinthoides non-scripta) poses a risk that is rather peculiar to Britain because, with only a couple of exceptions, it is only in Britain that the plant grows in great carpets across the woodland floor.Their lushness is enough to attract any hungry cow, especially as they are in leaf at just the time when the better meadows would have been set aside for a hay crop. Feeding on Bluebells instead of grass would cause the cow to dry up as the toxins took effect. They are glycosides, similar to those found in the Foxglove which are now exploited for heart medicines. It is possible, although no record has been traced so far, that when Bluebell bulbs were dug up as an important source of glue and laundry starch, the greenery was torn off and thrown to the cattle.

BRACKEN (Pteridium aquilinum) gets cited as Britain's worst weed, as it invades so many hectares of farmland every year. It was better controlled in the past when country people cut and used it for animal bedding. The cutting rights were exercised in August, when the ferns were divided into stands and left marked out for a week to see if any disputes arose. Then it was cut and left to dry before being brought home. Cutting it green weakened the plant and reduced its invasive vigour. These practices did not reduce the risk from this very hazardous plant as some of the powerful toxins which it contains persist after drying. Fortunately, such toxic bedding was not very palatable to the stock. Even green it is only eaten when there is a shortage of other feed, such as in the great drought of 1893 when it caused serious losses in cattle. It is toxic to humans too, being associated with tumours of the digestive system in countries where it is eaten, such as Japan, Canada and the north eastern United States. As a culinary item it is gathered as the croziers emerge in the spring and is thus marketed as 'fiddleheads' from the appearance.

Hedgerows are now valued again
for the diversity of their wildlife
and among their herbs, shrubs and
trees are a few the wise stockman
or dairymaid tried to keep from
the cattle.

HAWTHORN (Crataegus monogyna)
was the chief hedging tree long
before it came to be used so
universally after the Enclosure
Awards. It seems safe until
the haws are browsed off in
autumn. Then the urine becomes
stained and there is a distinct
drop in milk yield.

ASH (Fraxinus excelsior),
a choice main species from which
to grow the hedgerow standards,
defends itself admirably against
being eaten - rarely does an Ash
tree have nibbled leaves - but in
autumn the fallen leaves can cause
chronic illness in cattle. In the
Midlands this came to be known as
the "Wood Evil".

WHITE BRYONY (Bryonia dioica)
is a grand climber that shoots out
of the ground in the spring, clothes
the summer hedges with beautiful lobed
leaves and greenish white flowers until
it shrivels golden in the autumn when the
female plants are hung with bunches of brilliant
red berries. Anything that grand must be in league
with the Devil and so in France it is called 'navet
du diable' - Devil's Turnip. The turnip allusion
comes from the massive tuberous root, over half a
metre long and fanged so as to resemble a human body -
the famous English Mandrake of early medicine,

41

Alas the English presumed this plant would function as well as the true Mandrake (Mandragora officinalis) but it's a drastic purgative so that many of the doses recommended would have been lethal. Perhaps that was the very reassurance needed by anyone doubting the myth that to dig it up will cause it to scream and that anyone hearing the scream will drop dead. It is still used in medicine today but should not be administered by the amateur, only by the highly skilled, and not to the pregnant. This defies all tradition, that the herb is an aid to fertility - did not God make Leah fertile in a Mandrake story? (see Genesis XXX 14-21). This and fertility myths led dairymen to hang up the dried roots in the cowsheds to invoke good fortune upon the stock; one is now on display in the Gloucester Folk Museum.

After the harvest the cattle were turned out on the arable land to graze any weeds left after the crop had been taken.

FAT-HEN (Chenopodium album), although a mealy green would show up well and attract grazers. This plant accumulates nitrates but it is thought that it is the oxalates that cause the poisoning - they combine with the blood calcium to cause hypoglycaemia. Ironically this herb was used deliberately as cattle fodder. Its seeds have been eaten by man since Neolithic times until the 19th century and its leaves are sometimes suggested nowadays as being suitable for salads. In humans it can cause the skin to become sensitive to light with hideous-sounding results. It seems to be one of those cases of "a little of what you like does you good but you can have too much of a good thing." It's best to leave it alone - shame really, it's always satisfying to eat the garden weeds!

CORN POPPY (Papaver rhoeas) contains various alkaloids that are capable of terminating lactation but in Britain there are no recent records of such poisoning. Turning the cows out on to the stubble would have been safe as far as this plant is concerned as it would have been harvested with the corn and been devoid of basal leaves by that stage in its cycle. Only if stock strayed into the crowing crop would there have been a risk but even then the animals would have preferred to graze the corn as the poppy does not taste pleasant to them. On the other hand there would have been a lot of poppy in the crop because traditionally it was not weeded out; it was needed "for the good health of the crop". That's a belief that can be traced back to the Mother Earth fertility rites of prehistoric peoples. Later it was absorbed into the relevant Greek myths (read an explanation of the abduction of Persephone by Hades).

43

Out on the crop fields, or straying into them before harvest, had risks from the crops themselves. Potatoes that have been exposed to the light and gone green are toxic to cattle just as they are to humans. Fodder Beet, Sugar Beet and Mangel-wurzels (Mangolds) are all famous as cattle feed but only if used wisely; Onions, Garlic, and even Radishes can all upset cows.

SPEARMINT (Mentha spicata) was added to the feed if there was a need to suppress lactation deliberately. Mint hybridizes very readily and the different species have been in cultivation for so long that there are now thousands of different Mints to choose from but the Spearmint has always been one of the most widely grown and best known as a food additive for cattle. Today it is much used as a digestive aid for man and beast and this is ancient knowledge going back beyond the Romans. It was the Romans who came up with the notion that Mint would stop milk curdling in the stomach and so took the herb with any meal containing milk. It was said that steeping or infusing Mint in milk would prevent fermentation. This is probably correct as in the 18th century Dr. William Withering (the man who discovered the value of Foxgloves for heart conditions) recorded that milk could not be made into cheese if the cows had been eating **CORN MINT** (Mentha arvensis). There have been similar reports down the ages.

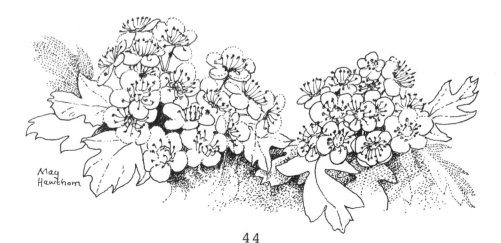

May
Hawthorn

44

MILKING

MINT (Mentha spp.) was used to purify
water and so may have been used in dairying.

PLANTS AND MILKING

Plants came into use as soon as it was milking time.
Wood was needed for pails, yokes, hoops and milking
stools and these were chosen from specific trees. Any
that were associated with evil, such as **ELDER** (Sambucus
nigra), were excluded automatically. Milk was known to
be vulnerarable to unseen forces - after all, it went
'off' for no apparent reason.

MILKING PAILS

In these days of metal and lightweight plastic for
buckets it is easy to forget the use of wood for such
items in the past. The records referred to during this
study used the word 'pail' rather than bucket, usually
in connection with liquids and having connections with
the notion of a measure. Buckets seemed to be more
general purpose utensils, for carrying solid and dry
materials, and could be square as well as round.

Handles were of rope and
that was made of **HEMP**
(Cannabis sativa) which
was once an important crop
(illegal nowadays). To
ensure maximum capacity
these were knotted into
two opposing staves
protruding higher than
the rim. There were also
piggins which had just
one stave extended upwards.
Not all the utensils had
handles. Early illustrations
show dairymaids carrying them
on their heads and for this
the pails were apparently
seated on protective wreaths
of twisted **GRASS**.

The cooper worked in two ways: slack and white. For the slack method the staves were bound with strips of wood or with a band of twisted stems, while for white coopering iron hoops were used. Those with hoops of iron were used for utensils destined to hold liquid while the slack method was used for dry materials. At least, that is what is said normally in the books but is not entirely correct. Some early illustrations relating to dairying show the slack method in use and this is not artists' licence or ignorance. Anyone who visits the Tudor kitchens at Hampton Court Palace at Christmas when they are put back into use will find slack coopered utensils being used for liquids and steaming hot liquids at that. Walk on from Wolsey's kitchen to the wine cellar and there will be found rows of wine barrels, all beautifully crafted by the slack method. The hoops are of split Hazel.

Some of the pails in the old illustrations are shown wider at the base than the rim, unlike today's. These were more stable on rough ground when cows were milked in the fields and they would have slopped less when the milk was brought back on pack horses.

WILLOW (Salix spp.) and **HAZEL** (Corylus avellana) provided the pliant stems for the binding hoops. Willow was sufficiently strong and flexible for the whole stem to be used. Hazel was best if a thicker stem was cleft into half. It was given a complete twist when used, to bring the flat cut surfaces together for fixing and because the spiralled fibres added to its strength. Alternatively several stems were twisted together like a rope. These were known in some dialects, such as in Surrey, as withes; a Saxon term which is still understood by the older generation today. It is related to the better known word withy.

Choosing wood for milk pails took into account such requirements as resistance to wetting and drying, without warping and splitting. It must be close-grained so as not to trap a residue that would contaminate the next filling and it must suit being scoured out. It must not itself contaminate the milk by yielding dye as would **ALDER** (Alnus glutinosa), nor taste and smell as would Elder or the turpentine in coniferous wood. Pale wood was preferred for cleanliness; dairy hygiene was taken into account at an earlier date than is popularly believed.

OAK, (Quercus robur and Quercus petraea) was most frequently chosen, it being worked up from staves in a half-barrel fashion using coopering skills. Apart from satisfying the requirements listed above, Oak was also readily available and was of course, famously durable. The disadvantages of Oak were that it can be dark in colour and it is one of our heavier woods. When full an oaken pail would have been a considerable weight to lift and carry.

ASH (Fraxinus excelsior), is a lighter wood that was readily available but few references to its use for pails have been traced. This is due most probably to it being porous and therefore likely to hold a contaminating residue. In coopering the porous nature would not have been so important if the barrel was intended for powder.

48

Any leaking joints could be sealed with coagulating juice boiled out of **NETTLES** (Urtica dioica). The pail was scoured round with handfuls of **HORSETAIL** (Equisetum spp.), or, near Southern heaths and Northern moors, scouring brushes were made up from **HEATHER** (Calluna vulgaris).

MILKING STOOLS

The popular notion of milking a cow into a pail, by hand, sitting on a three-legged stool is founded upon centuries of fact. It is thought that the three-legged stool is the oldest item of constructed furniture. It is the design rather than the timber that is vital, for only a three-legged stool is stable upon uneven surfaces, such as that of the pastures where the cows were milked. Nevertheless, the **SYCAMORE** (Acer pseudoplatanus) has been listed for this service. No doubt this is due to its high reputation for providing quality dairying items.

YOKES

Yokes need no introduction. Peasants carrying pails on a yoke is as familiar an image of past rural life as peasants wearing smocks.

The weight of two full pails is considerable and so the timber for the yoke needs to be strong, in the sense of being flexible, to 'give' a little under the strain. It needs to be light itself and readily shaped, to suit the wearer. One example proved a perfect fit and was surprisingly comfortable.

ASH, (Fraxinus excelsior) is Britain's supreme timber for this tensile strength and has always been cited as best for yokes; those examined have been of this wood. In ancient times, according to John Evelyn quoting Virgil, LIME (Tilia spp) was used. It is one of the best woods for carving so it responded well to being shaped to fit the shoulders. Evelyn himself lists HORNBEAM (Carpinus betulus) the strongest of British timbers, being more resistant to cleaving than Oak. Maybe such references are to yokes on oxen being worked as draught animals. Evelyn, however, specifies 'ox yokes' on other occasions.

HOOPS

A hoop was placed across the tops of pails to be carried on a yoke. This held the pails apart at the handles to prevent them swinging against the legs of the carrier, who walked inside the hoop.

ASH or **HAZEL** (Corylus avellana) provided the strong pliant stems which were converted by the hooper. He was a craftsman who worked out in the Ash and Hazel copses and was once so significant as to give rise to the surname. These hoops can be spotted in many a painting of rural life; a French painting seen shows not a hoop but a square frame of battens nailed crudely together.

MILKING TODAY

The milking machines of today use materials far removed from those of our ancestors and are designed to exclude contact with the air. The first machines were developed in the late 19th century but it is disputed whether they were an American or a Scottish invention. There was a long period of trial-and-error before a serviceable machine was achieved owing to the special way a calf extracts milk from the teat - by pulling gently as well as sucking, which proved a difficult action to simulate. The early attempts drew more blood down into the teats than milk into the pail. Continuous modification lasted until the First World War.

51

By then the job of carrying the sealed pails from the stalls to the dairy had been made redundant (although still performed on some farms today) by a new system whereby the milk was piped direct from the cow to the dairy. It means the milk has little or no contact with the air whereas in earlier days there was ample opportunity for flies, cow hairs and other unsavoury objects to fall into the milk.

BUTTER-MAKING

If soured cream is agitated it will turn into butter.
It sounds so simple but it can be punishing! Many a
child's misdemeanours resulted in the arm-aching task
of rotating the butter churn - slop slop slop.

Firstly the milk was left to stand so that the cream
would float to the top, so a container with a large
surface area rather than great depth was best. It was
also easier to skim the resulting top layer off.
Readers brought up on standardised 'shop' milk
will have little appreciation of the thick
yellowy layer that gradually rose to the
surface.

The cream was then skimmed deftly off,
using a flat-bottomed scoop of metal or
wood. These were perforated so as to
allow the thinner milk to run through as
the cream was lifted. Where the skimmer
scraped the bottom it tended to wear
down the front edge. When these skimmers
are made of metal the worn front edge
makes it easier to spot their true
identity when offered mistakenly as
'chestnut roasters' in antique shops.
Wooden skimmers were made from **SYCAMORE**
(Acer pseudoplatanus) from the 17th
century onwards.

SYCAMORE (Acer pseudoplatanus) holds the prime position in providing wood for dairy utensils. It is not, however, a native tree. It comes from Central and Southern Europe but at what date it was introduced has been the subject of much debate. Some have asserted that it was one of the trees present before the last Ice Age but no archaeological evidence for that was recorded by Godwin for his 'History of the British Flora'. That it was introduced by the Romans has not been substantiated, nor the all too familiar notion that it was brought back by the medieval Crusaders. The vexed question was researched by E.Jones in 1944 (Journal of Ecology, 32:2) who found it was very rare or absent in the 16th century. Then it quickly found popularity, running into the 17th century.

Part of the difficulty for researchers is that Sycamore was often the name given to the Fig and fig was a medieval term for haemorrhoids!

The Tudors and Stuarts found the Sycamore much to their liking. It casts dense shade, for which it is so often condemned today, but which was a delight for those people to walk through. John Evelyn enthuses again and again in his 'Silva' over the trees that created shaded walks. Then there was an enthusiasm for specimen trees planted in parkland settings and the Sycamore grows fast when young to encourage landowners of the wisdom of their choice. Soon, especially in Scotland, there were large specimens ready to yield timber.

The timber from a single mature Sycamore trunk can be considerable. Soon it was being tried for a wide range of purposes but its very whiteness suggested uses in kitchen and dairy, where hygiene was important. Our ancestors had more respect for hygiene than we deign to give them. Milk soon 'goes off' under dirty conditions and the close-grained Sycamore wood absorbed less residue than some woods. It was also easy to shape; indeed, it could be shaped unseasoned, straight from the green. Bowls could be readily formed on a lathe by the turner or simply hollowed out from the solid with an adze. Lastly, it has no dye, taste or smell by which it can contaminate the milk. It's unrivalled for dairying.

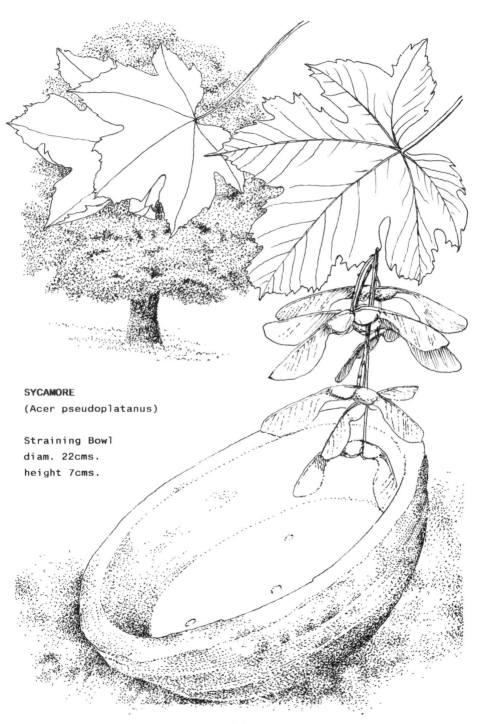

SYCAMORE

(Acer pseudoplatanus)

Straining Bowl
diam. 22cms.
height 7cms.

Turn-over churn;
hand-made bowl and jug.

Cream from which to make the butter was set aside so that it would start to turn sour. Skill is required to judge the moment to begin churning, for if souring proceeds too far then the butter too will taste sour. Another method was to stir in some cream that was already sour and then the bacteria set to work quickly. The cream was then kept moving until little beads of butter began to appear, at which point cold water was added and churning continued for several more minutes. Finally the churn contained a mixture of butter and the watery milky liquid, known as butter-milk. The latter was drained off and used by man and beast. The butter was removed and divided up for use, storage, or sale.

At this stage the butter-pats or Scotch hands/handles were used to pat the butter into a more solid mass and then to shape it up into portions. Again our ancestors learned exactly how to get the best and so when they shaped their pieces of wood into the pats they tapered them slightly away from the handle, into wedges. Modern pats do not usually have this taper and this slight difference makes all the difference; modern pats do not work so easily as do the older design.

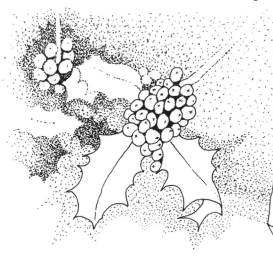

Despite what is usually said about the strength of the wavy grain of **ELM** this was a wood avoided for butter pats as they were liable to snap at the shoulders. **BEECH** was a popular cheap choice but for finer quality there was **BOX** and **HOLLY**. The chief limitation was whether the wood, once moistened, was likely to leave splinters or fibres in the butter.

BOX (Buxus sempervirens) is familiar to garden lovers as a hedging shrub, especially in the days of formal gardens when low hedges were used to enclose areas for plants or coloured gravels. If left unclipped it will grow into a small but very distinctive evergreen tree of garden merit. It has been out of horticultural fashion for a century but is now receiving deserved attention again. One reason for it falling from favour is the scent given off in winter sunshine or when clipped. This has always been contentious; John Evelyn (1664) observed, "Its scent is not agreeable to many: if immediately upon clipping (when only it is most offensive) you water it, the smell vanishes, and is no more considerable." By watering it he means spray it, but many of us enjoy the scent.

Left uncut it reaches, eventually, some 5m or more in height, although in the wild it tends to grow in groves where the trunks lean and writhe through the tree's self-created darkness. This is a rare sight today as the tree in the wild has been exploited for its timber to the point where it is a national rarity. It can be found in Buckinghamshire, Kent, Gloucestershire and Surrey which has the most famous groves of all around Box Hill. Elsewhere place-names testify to its former existence.

Foreign imports were needed to satisfy the demand for this hard, white, close-grained wood, which was so solid and unyielding that it was ideal for tasks demanding accuracy, whether being engraved for making book illustrations or for mathematical and musical instruments. It had at least 27 uses including butter pats. The wood is so dense that it will not float and had the distinction of being sold by weight not volume.

Box tree
Rarely grown as a
specimen tree as
growth it so irregular.

Having portioned out the butter the next task was to stamp it with a personal design that would act as a trade mark in the market place. Wooden butter prints are therefore of endless variety as they were specific to their farm. They were passed down from generation to generation. Designs ranged from abstract geometry through to stylised motifs from reality. Cows were a popular motif but the flowers of the farm were featured too.

Gertrude Jekyll (Old West Surrey; 1904) lists roses and forget-me-nots, corn and twigs of apples. The last was appropriate if **APPLE** (Malus pumila, M.sylvestris) was the wood from which was made the block. Fruit-tree wood is hard and close-grained so it both carves and wears well, making it of commercial importance in the past. Some of the medieval tenancy agreements specify the regular planting of fruit trees, sometimes yearly, so fruit trees must have been felled just as regularly for their timber. Certainly its hardness gave rise to many uses, from mallet heads to mill wheel cogs but particularly carved and turned items.

Butter
Prints

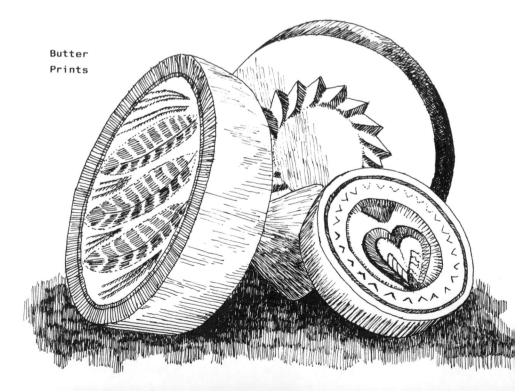

HOLLY (Ilex aquifolium)
is another hard, close-grained
wood which is also very white
for hygiene purposes. At first
it is greenish but as it ages
it becomes the whitest British
wood of all. Thus it too was
available widely on the market.
The furniture-makers wanted it
for inlay work (important in
Tunbridge Ware for example). The
textile industries wanted it for
printing blocks (particularly for
calico imported plain from India)
not only because it was white enough
to show up the colours but because, like
Box, it will not warp and twist when wetted
and it therefore gave an even print. Then too
it was available as a by-product of the workers
who needed the bark for making the most effective
of British bird-limes - was once an important product.

Holly wood had at least 15 specific uses. No wonder
C.P.Johnson could observe in 1862, "In England the tree
is usually small, rarely found growing to more than the
size of a large bush, a circumstance partly to be
accounted for by the value of the timber, which caused
the larger trees to be felled in old times when the wood
of the kind was in greater comparative demand than at
present."

(The Useful Plants of Great Britain)

Wrapping the butter was the next demand upon the dairymaid's floral knowledge. Only comparatively recently has paper been available, in sizes large enough, and affordable (it used to be taxed). Large leaves solved the problem for many centuries before that and the British plant with the largest leaves was the Butterbur (or Butterburn or Butter Dock).

BUTTERBUR (Petasites hybridus) has leaves that can grow up to 90cm across. Consequently in Somerset it has been known as Wild Rhubarb or Turkey Rhubarb. A lot of butter can be wrapped in a Butterbur leaf! People can also shelter from the rain under one and that's how it got its generic name - from the Greek petasos, a wide-brimmed hat, hence it is known in Yorkshire and Somerset as Umbrella Plant.

Butterbur grows along the riversides and in other wet places, especially in the North. It is very hardy and starts flowering in March. This makes it important for feeding bees when other spring flowers are scarce. Thus it may have been grown deliberately near hives, as was done in Sweden. The flowers appear before the leaves but once the latter have started to blow they are easy to find simply by way of their size. In the south east of England, however, it is a rare or scarce plant, so another plant had to be used for wrapping butter. **COLTSFOOT** has been suggested. Certainly its country names include both Butter and Butterbur.

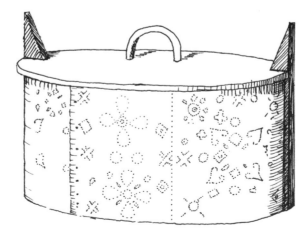

Butter
Box

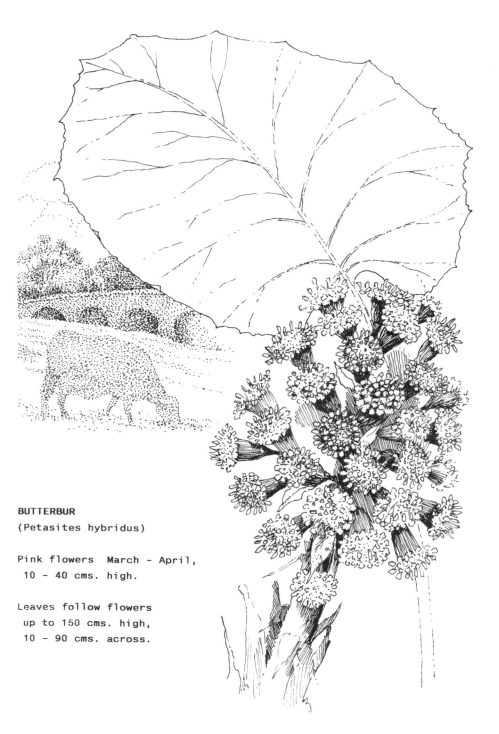

BUTTERBUR

(Petasites hybridus)

Pink flowers March - April,
10 - 40 cms. high.

Leaves follow flowers
up to 150 cms. high,
10 - 90 cms. across.

COLTSFOOT (Tussilago farfara) is easily spotted in early spring when roadsides bear patches or drifts of the brazen yellow flowers, like small Dandelions. Only later do the leaves appear and develop their whitish hoary coating. People likened them to the White Poplar when it was known as Farfarus, hence its botanical specific name. Tussilago was its Roman name, from the Latin 'tussis' for cough. This was and still is, used as a powerful herb in the treatment of coughs, giving rise to the medical term (anti)tussive, meaning to relieve coughs. The synonym, bechic, comes from this plant's Greek name, Bechion. The Coltsfoot has been a well-known and important herb for thousands of years.

As a wrapping for butter, it would seem to be a safe plant to so use, for although it is not regarded as having great antibiotic constituents, it is widely held to be anti-inflammatory and so for all those thousands of years it has been employed as a wound herb and for using as a poultice. So important was this herb that the French apothecaries chose it as their trade mark, painting the flowers onto the door posts of their Paris shops. It is also highly nutritive and has been listed among the wild plants that people can cull for free food BUT IT SHOULD NOT BE EATEN.

Coltsfoot

Seale, 54

CHEESE-MAKING

Every farmhouse made its cheeses in the past. They were a way of preserving a dairy product, by way of heavy salting, into the winter when there was no milk due to poor feeding and the end of the lactation cycle. In theory the making of cheese is very simple. In practice the making of a cheese that is fit to eat is very difficult.

The difficulty with making good cheese arose over the number of variables involved. These have all been standardised in today's factory cheeses so we know exactly what to expect every single time but farmhouse cheeses in the past were never quite the same twice. The level of acidity and the micro-organisms working in the unpasteurised milk were two crucial factors over which there was no understanding.

More obvious variables included whether the milk was from sheep, goats or cows; since the end of the 16th century the English cheeses came predominantly from cow milk. Important too was the time of milking - evening milk is richer than morning. Double Gloucester is a mixture of the two. The season made a difference, with summer being best, and then there was the pasturage upon which the animals grazed, with flowery meadows being preferred.

Some farms and even whole districts got it down to a fine art, such as Caerphilly, Cheddar, Cheshire, Gloucester, Lancashire and Leicester. Other places were famed for the foulness of their cheese, especially in the south east, whether north of the Thames in Essex and Suffolk or south of it in Kent and Surrey.

It was all a matter of "art", as recorded in this 17th century account from Worplesdon in Surrey:-
"The cheese of this, as well as some other parts of this County is very bad and poor: They rob their Cheese by taking out the Butter for London, and they are miserably ignorant as to Dairy (except for Butter.) A Gentlewoman of Cheshire, married into these parts (near Albury) and misliking the Cheese here, sent a Dairy-Maid out of her own Country, but she could not with all her Cheshire Skill make any good Cheese here" but a lady from Wiltshire "makes as good Cheese here as ever she did in her own Country, viz. that sort of Cheese which is call'd in London, Marlborough Cheese, about an Inch thick, and tells me, 'Tis only want of Art."
(John Aubrey, Natural History and Antiquities
of the County of Surrey, Vol.III, pp 326-7)

To make cheese the milk must curdle and that will happen on a hot day when the milk goes sour. The curds can be strained out to make the original soft cheese. The longest serving plant for making the strainer or 'sile' has over six dozen English names but is now best known as Goosegrass or Cleevers;-

GOOSEGRASS (Galium aparine)
This weed, of culinary and medicinal value, loves soil rich in phosphates and is thus an indicator plant of man's activities. It would always have been abundant around farmsteads, although horses, cows and sheep all relish it. The hooked bristles of its fruits caught in the fur and spread the seeds around (unless gathered by man for brewing a type of tea; its close relation is the coffee tree). Despite having quite large fruits the flowers are tiny little white stars, overlooked by passers-by.

Back in the first century AD Dioscorides recorded the Greek shepherds using mats of the plant to sieve their milk. In the 18th century the famous Swedish botanist known as Linnaeus observed the Swedes were still doing the same and apparently Goosegrass sieves were still in use this century. The reason this plant was chosen above all others was due to the way the multitudes of tiny hooks all over the growth will interlock to make a strong self-adherering mat. Its specific name 'aparine' comes from the Greek word 'aparo' meaning to seize. There is an abundance of English names referring to this clinging action, including Catchweed, Clinging Sweethearts, Grip Grass, Hedgehogs, Snares, Stick Buttons, Stickyback, Sticky Willy and Tethers.

Making soft cheese this way risks infection with such harmful bacteria as Listeria. However, juices of certain plants will curdle milk while it's still fresh. Such 'vegetable rennets' make "soft" cheese. The "hard" cheeses employ animal rennet, obtained from the lining of the fourth stomach of a calf, within two weeks of birth, so that it's still feeding on milk. The rennet, being an enzyme, aids digestion. Although calves are best known for providing this, lambs used to be the prime source. The animal tissue was dipped into the heated milk.

VEGETABLE RENNETS

Our ancestors needed their livestock to grow on so animal rennet from calves and lambs must always have been scarce. Some vegetable juices were coagulants, exploited as styptics to clot the blood of open wounds as well as to curdle milk.

Curdlers included **THISTLE** flowers, **ARTICHOKES**, seeds of **SAFFRON** (very expensive so unlikely to have been used in practice), **FIG** tree sap, **GOAT'S RUE** (Galega officinalis) which was also used as a galactogogue, **NIPPLEWORT** (Lapsana communis) which is more likely to have been used in ointment treatment of infected, sore or injured teats and the **MADDERS** (Rubia tinctoria) or the inferior British **WILD MADDER** (Rubia peregrina). The Madders were primarily dye plants, with known medicinal values. They would have tinted cheeses pink and seem to have been little used. The **LADY'S BEDSTRAW** was the most important:-

LADY'S BEDSTRAW
(Galium verum)
Some of the choice vegetable rennets are from plants belonging to the genus Galium, (gala is Greek for milk), including Galium aparine, Goosegrass, referred to above, which contains a blend of three acids. Thus among its country names it is known as Cheese Rennet or Cheese Rennet Herb. Of much greater importance, because it was stronger, was Galium verum, known today as Lady's Bedstraw but also collected as Cheese Renning or Cheese Rennet Herb. In 1st century Greece it was known to Dioscorides as simply Galion - Milk Plant.

It contains the enzyme rennin which has been used since at least the time of the Ancient Greeks until the 19th century. It was the vital ingredient that made the esteemed Cheshire cheese better than others made without it. Similarly, it was used for the Gloucester cheeses, in conjunction with Stinging Nettles.

It was so important that it had to be Christianised to keep it in acceptable use. Thus it became a "cradle herb" - one of the herbs in the manger at Christ's Nativity. One version of the myth has the bedding being a mixture of two herbs but at the birth of Christ only one rose up in Adoration so God cursed the one that did not. It was forbidden to flower ever again. It was the Bracken fern. The other plant hailed the birth with a burst of flower, so God blessed it by changing the white blooms to gold. It was Our Lady's Bedstraw but with the rise of Protestantism the 'Our' was dropped as being too Romanist.

Although that is a popular myth it is based upon an error. The name was given it by Lyte in 1578 when he translated Unser Frauen Betstro from German herbals but there it was being used for an entirely different plant, the Thyme, which doesn't even have gold flowers.

It was not necessary to extract the juice separately from the rennet herbs. The milk was heated and the whole plant plunged into it. Then it had to be stroked to keep the cream down while the rennet did its work. The Lady's Bedstraw released a yellowish green dye, giving rise to green cheeses. The flowering tops could be used on their own and then it was a gold dye that came out, to give the familiar colour to Cheshire cheese etc. It was used right up until the 18th century, when it was superceded by a new introduction, annatto, E160(b), made from the seeds of Bixa orellana, a Brazilian rainforest tree.

Unidentified item from dairy. Rennet stirrer?

CARLINE THISTLES (Carlina spp.)

Other vegetable rennets were available. References to thistles are most likely to be to the dwarf Carline Thistle. The best was Calina acaulis but this is a Continental species, not found in Britain. It would get itself into British knowledge through our habit of translating European herbals. There is a British species, Carlina vulgaris, which although inferior, could be pressed into service.

The flowers, if not gathered for food like artichokes, would dry and persist as one of the 'everlastings'. As so few flowers do this naturally, they were revered, and so the early Saxons apparently used it in their pagan chants. Consequently it had to be Christianised to keep it in use and so we read that an angel responded to the prayers of Charlemagne and showed him the herb that would cure his ailing army. Medicinally, Carlina acaulis has quite a list of attributes but it is not very powerful; the British one less so.

Despite having spiny leaves, it was known to farmers as a plant that would stimulate the appetite of cattle. It was used on the farmers themselves by herbalists as an aid to digestion. This was well founded as the plant contains antibiotics. Their antibacterial action has implications for the cheese-maker when using the leaves of this plant for their rennet action.

71

TEASELS (Dipsacus spp.)

The juice of Teasel flowers, Dipsacus fullonum and Dipsacus sativus, have also been claimed as a rennets. Usage must have been very limited as the seed heads were a crop of importance until very recent times. They were needed in the woollen textile industry. The dried seed heads, once bunched and tied, were bound together onto poles for rolling over the cloth to tease or fluff up the weave. A decade ago, pleas for the heads were still being issued by manufacturers of high-class knit-wear as no machine could do the job better.

STINGING NETTLES (Urtica dioica)

Stinging Nettles were very important to man for a wide range of purposes. As far as cheese-making is concerned it is the coagulating qualities of the sap that were of significance. Not only was it one of the most powerful of styptics to seal a bleeding wound but its coagulent properties were exploited to seal leaking sinks and vessels in the dairy and to curdle milk.

It works best once it has been boiled in a strong salt solution, which was not a disadvantage as the salt acted as a preservative in the cheese. The green dye came out of the plant to colour the cheese but refined use overcame this if required, as in Gloucestershire's cheeses.

VEGETABLE RENNET TODAY

The use of vegetable rennets has increased in recent times for a combination of reasons. Customers, mindful of animal welfare, have brought about a decline in the use of veal and therefore of the numbers of calves being reared to provide animal rennet. Then there is the increasing demand for vegetarian products and for products that will not offend religious doctrines of Jews, Hindus etc.

All is not what it seems however. The "vegetable" rennets of today are not, strictly speaking, made from plants. They are products of genetic engineering since the scientists have been able to isolate the gene responsible for the enzymes (known as chymosins) and have learned how to culture them in bacteria or fungal moulds to yield quantities of the chymosins. Although this isolates the compounds from animals the genes are of animal origin. Similarly, the moulds in which they are cultured are no longer vegetable, since scientists have now decided fungi are not plants. They are classified as a third group after animals and plants.

Food labelling has not yet caught up with science. There has been a reluctance to use the word mould for fear of it causing unwarranted fears in consumers. This is not very sound as consumers accept already yeast for baking and brewing, Penicillium in antibiotic medicines, and mould for flavouring in cheeses like Danish Blue. There were high level discussions taking place to resolve these problems at the time this section was being prepared in 1993.

73

COLOUR AND FLAVOUR

Colouring cheese was largely a matter of chance. Looks didn't count and some of the cheeses must have looked an awful motley of greens and blues and yellows. No wonder the Lady's Bedstraw, imparting its stronger yellow in a cheese that should not have green juice nor blue mould in it, won such favour. Only in recent times and in noble households did appearances count.

Flavour was another matter. It is not difficult to imagine how some counties became renowned for their foul cheese. Adding strong tasting herbs would seem sensible and easy but in practice was not nearly so simple. Some of the most popular flavours contain chemicals that upset the action of the very micro-organisms needed to create cheese. This applied to the most popular flavourings: **GARLIC, LEEK** and **ONION.** All were grown widely in the past; so much so that the Saxons called a vegetable plot a leek-yard. Onion has retained its universal popularity and is now the most widely used flavouring herb in the world. Today too we have mastered the art of adding it successfully to cheese.

SAGE (Salvia officinalis) was another healing herb; Salvia means healing (as in salve for ointment) while its official recognition is recorded in its specific name, officinalis. It is thus not only tasty to use but in cheeses, stuffing, etc. helped to counteract food poisoning. Its leaves are anti-bacterial and anti-fungal. They are therefore capable of inhibiting the process of cheese-making if added at the wrong stage. Once added it acted as a preservative although salt was the chief agent for that.

74

Bringing on
the next
generation.

CURDS AND WHEY

After curdling the milk the next
operation is to strain out remaining
whey from the curds. The mixture is
emptied into a whey bowl or 'stele'
which has a central drainage hole,
covered by a mesh, allowing the whey
to drip through into another bowl beneath.
The two bowls are held apart by a wooden frame
or 'brig' which straddles the bowl beneath. The
brig illustrated was of BEECH (Fagus sylvatica) which
is light and serviceable and is still the commonest
hardwood in use in British homes today. All wooden
things were liable to be shaped by the craftsman in
such a way as to reduce weight without reducing
strength. Thus the cabinet makers and the wheelwrights,
the cartwrights and wainwrights all produced works of
noted elegance but see here how the craftsmanship of
the village carpenter demanded that he do just the same
with something as mundane as a bowl rack for a dairy.

ABOVE - The brig in use. The one illustrated was
some 60cm long by 27 cm wide but size varied according
to need, relating to the size of bowls in use. These in
turn did not necessarily relate to standard measures,
as might well be the case today.

Beech

Most bowls were made of wood rather than pottery, even for dairying, because they were cheaper and wouldn't break. They were standard employment for the turner or carpenter. This all changed when the Industrial Revolution created mass-produced clay wares from The Potteries in the 'Black Country' of the English Midlands. An effective canal system of transportation ensured pottery became far cheaper and more readily available throughout so much of the country.

ELM
bowl
made with an adze.
Diam. 26cm x 25cm; circum. 80.5cm; height 9cm.

CHEESE PRESSES

The most important apparatus associated with cheese-making was the press by which surplus fluid (whey) was removed. This was either drunk on the farm or else fed to the pig. The latter doesn't sound very significant today but to our ancestors the family pig was of the utmost importance as food. The family fed the pig all summer and the pig fed the family all winter.

Cheese presses were of various designs and sizes. In Somerset, around Cheddar, farmers created a very early example of co-operative farming with individual producers pooling their milk to be made into massive cheeses of 120 pounds. At the other extreme, small cheeses could be processed in a press similar to the one illustrated, both parts of which are made of **OAK**.

OAK (Quercus robur and Q. petraea) was not popular for utensils, being heavy and laborious to shape. There were times when its strength, weight and durability were needed and such was the case with cheese presses. Small ones were walled with Oak laminate, bound with iron to stop the join springing apart when the curds are being pressed or 'pitched'.

The joins could be sealed with Nettle juice. The disc is also oaken because it needs to be heavy. Extra weights could be stacked on top when needed. It is called a "follower" or a "sinker", as it follows the sinking contents, as the whey squeezes out through small piercings. A similar press of **ELM** has been seen also.

Quercus
robur

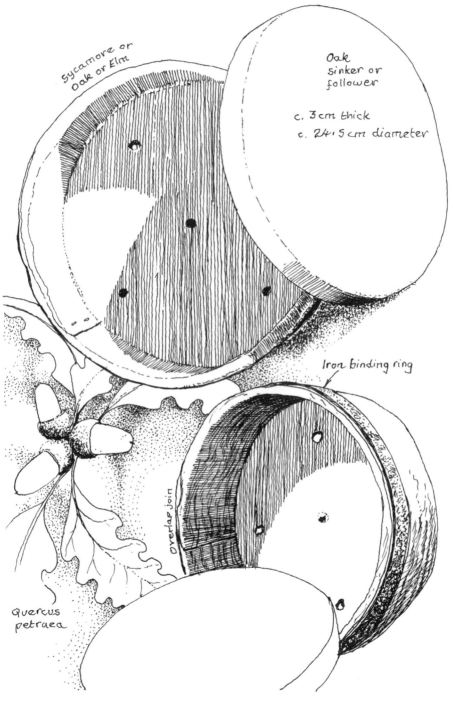

Sycamore or
Oak or Elm

Oak
sinker or
follower

c. 3 cm thick

c. 24.5 cm diameter

Iron binding ring

Overlap join

Quercus
petraea

ELM (Ulmus spp. and hybrids) was
used regularly instead of oak for
the vats, presses and moulds which,
by the 18th century, were called
'chessels'. It is now so long since
Dutch Elm Disease swept through
Britain in the 1970s that many
readers will not remember these
grand trees, taller than broad
and always distinctive whether
bare or in leaf. Millions of
them were dotted along the
field boundaries, especially
on the plains of heavier soils.
Only those who remember them will
comprehend the anguish expressed
in those years as more and more of
the grand silhouettes turned brown,
withered and died. For hundreds of
years these were the nation's
reserves of timber, ready to be
cropped whenever needed and always
ready to sprout again from the
rootstock. These clones must have
been thousands of years old, going
right back to the end of the last
Ice Age. Now those same rootstocks
are sprouting again. When the new
trees reach flowering size their
bark is thick enough to attract
the beetles that spread the fungal
disease. They die again. Despite
fears and lamentations this is part
of the natural cycle of the countryside.
The relationship between fungus, beetle
and Elm tree has been traced through
documentary and then archaeological
evidence right back into prehistoric
times. There have been many epidemics
but the Elms always survive.

Elms were an abundant source of timber on a large scale; beams for barns, massive thick floor boards for houses, thinner weatherboarding and coffin planks. It is reputed to be very resistant to water and is thus ideal for dairies and other wet places. This is not entirely true. Elm will resist rotting only if kept perpetually wet; repeated wetting and drying causes rapid deterioration. This is why the building trades never used it for timber-framing except for internal structures or where the rain could be kept off by a protection of plastering or by tile-hanging. Stripping off the cladding to expose the timbers is now fashionable and many a cottage shows the silvery wavy grain of its Elm timbering but not for long, unless carefully treated. It is this wavy grain that strengthens the wood against splitting and so was used where it had to take up a strain, whether in wheel hubs, windmills, watermills or cheese presses. Other gains relating to food are that it does not taste, smell or release dye to contaminate the food.

PROTECTIVE PLANTS

As the sun sets the lowing of the cattle draws
attention to their penned state, in the pathway of
smoke drifting on the summer air from a smouldering
bonfire. The cattle are wearing wreaths of herbs around
their necks while around the fire, the villagers hold
handfuls of herbs into the smoke to preserve them. They
are known as the 'Herbs of St.John' and include Fennel,
one of the nine sacred herbs of the Saxons, described
elsewhere in this study. These will be hung up in the
homes and outbuildings to protect man and beast from
all evil. This sounds as though it comes from the far
distant past but this is a Christian ritual, albeit
with pagan origins. This is the Midsummer celebration
of the Eve and Feast of St.John the Baptist on June
23rd and 24th.

ST.JOHN'S WORT (Hypericum perforatum) was the most
magical plant used in these Midsummer celebrations
being the most highly esteemed for warding off evil.
Once treated in the holy smoke it was hung up in the
home and the cowshed. Additionally it was hung in the
dairy and put around milk churns. It was the main plant
used in the wreaths round the necks of the cows. A mass
of Christian mythology centred upon this plant although
there is an absence of early country names and folk
tales, suggesting it was adopted much later than many,
probably not till the 13th century. The plant contains
a red, flourescent pigment (Hypericin) which was said
to be the blood of John the Baptist (or of Christ) but
ironically it's toxic to cattle, causing primary
photosensitivity of the skin. In bright sunlight it
causes stock to develop bald patches and skin lesions.
Fortunately prolonged bright sunlight can be scarce in
Britain but in some countries where St.John's Wort has
been introduced (and become invasive) it is responsible
for serious economic losses. The plant is not safe in
hay either as drying destroys only 80% of the hypericin.

St. John's Wort
growing up through brambles.

Mrs Pennington
separating cream
with modern
centrifuge.

IVY (Hedera helix) was another of the 'Herbs of St. John', of interest to this study for being used in the same way as Hypericum - hung up in buildings and put under milk vessels, primarily in France; in Britain it was used more at Christmas and probably May Day.

Using plants like Holly and Ivy to celebrate Christmas is familiar enough but using plants to ward off evil may seem strange to present-day Christians. Earlier Christians, however, took the Biblical warnings about Satan very seriously and had a strong belief in Hell and perpetual Damnation. A peep into the church at Chaldon, Surrey to see the enormous painting on this theme that stretches right across the west wall will leave no doubt of this. It shows, with startling clarity and conviction, souls being pitched off the Purgatorial Ladder to fall down into the jaws of Hell, with all the associated Torments etc. It was painted about 1200, when the Herbs of St.John' were considered all important.

Another vital theme that is difficult for many modern readers to take seriously is the belief in the "little people". Scoff at the idea of fairies if you wish but they were nevertheless very real to our ancestors, right up to the twentieth century. It was not so long ago that people were putting down a saucer of milk in the dairy, for the Brownies, so that they would not steal from the settling bowls. The practices that we dismiss casually as 'superstition' today were once the observances and rites that had evolved from prehistoric religions. That trees should figure prominently is not surprising when many cultures, from the Greek to the Norse, believed mankind was descended from trees.

The Vikings believed that men came from an Ash while women were descended from an Elm. Tree worship was prohibited by King Canute in the 11th century, implying that five hundred years after Christianity came to England with St.Augustine, tree or ancestor worship was still so prevalent as to need suppressing by the law of the land. It has not been successful; people still say "touch wood" when making rash forecasts.

Touching wood was worth a fortune in the Middle Ages if the wood happened to be a holy relic, a piece of Christ's Cross, within reach of any pilgrim able to make a 'donation'.

Pagan trees still exert their influence into the 20th century. In 1993 people were reporting from West Surrey that they ask a Rowan before cutting it; others recorded a sense of great unease when the 1987 hurricane brought down their garden Rowan. The spirit of the trees can be very ambivalent in disposition, being both loyal friend and fearsome foe. Treated with respect and courtesy they would provide a good protection service.

ROWAN (Sorbus aucuparia) was the greatest friend by virtue of it being, to the Teutonic peoples, the most powerful protection against evil:-

> "Rowan trees and red thread
> Hold all witches in their dread"

or words to that effect. It was so widely known that most regions had their own version. This was the tree that was planted beside the house for protection or by the garden gate to prevent evil approaching the home, or by the outside toilet for obvious reasons! Its very name, Rowan, is believed by some to have come from the Norse 'runa' for a magical charm. It's been said that to break off a piece is to hold power in your hands for a thousand purposes and it certainly seems like that to read down a list of its former applications.

A great many references centre around dairying. As with other trees, it was hung up in dairies and in cowsheds, or nailed to the stalls. It was put inside empty milk vessels to keep evil out, or when they were in use Rowan was hung round the outside. The wooden stirring stick for the milk was supposed to be made from it (but see Hazel below). Rowan wood was supposed to be incorporated into the milk and butter churns, and to be used for the staffs for the butter churns. Even the cattle themselves had it twined between their horns or had to wear wreaths of it around their necks.

Rowan (Sorbus aucuparia)

According to one
description the
defender of the
Rowan has one red
eye in a black face,
crooked teeth and a
large nose. He's a
large-boned fellow.

When it came to moving stock then they were always considered at greatest risk and so all husbandmen and drovers sought out Rowan suckers from which to make their goad/gad.

> "Woe to the lad
> Without a Rowan-tree gad."

Hitting an animal with anything else was certain to knock evil into it so that it would lose weight and sicken. Most fearful of all in this context was the famous 'Evil Eye' but Rowan would keep that at bay too and was doing so well into the 20th century.

Significant was the tree's red berries. Red was sacred to the Norse god Thor and feared by evil forces. Red berries were caught up in the sacredness of red food which in some cultures, such as those of ancient Greece, was the preserve of the gods.

ELDER (Sambucus niger) has always been the most sinister of plants; not only did the Elder-spirit protect the tree but WAS the tree, so it was another one to be asked before cutting it.

Woodsmen feared cutting it by mistake and there were so many taboos on the use of the wood that rarely was it saleable, and, whatever happened it must not be burned. In 1956 there was a commotion when villagers spotted Elder wood in the faggots waiting to go into their village bakery. Nevertheless, used respectfully, it was a valuable raw material.

When it came to dairying the Elder was of more use than for any other occupation. In protecting itself the Elder warded off all other evil and so it was the most potent to plant outside the cow shed and dairy, usually by doors and windows. Many such places still have their Elders; seeing as the tree does not live to a great age, the practice if not the belief, must have lasted until very recent times. They can still be seen outside bakehouses too where they formerly safeguarded the dough from the devil; loaves still have the top crust split, to let the devil out.

Elder
Sambucus nigra

This is one tradition that does have some validity. The Elder smells strongly and somewhat offensively. This acts as a fly repellant and helped safeguard the milk. Butter muslin and any other dairy cloths were spread over the Elder to dry so that they would absorb the protective spirit (sympathetic magic) but the sceptical would say they picked up the smell.

Two other points: the cattle drovers carried Elder twigs, cut neatly through the nodes top and bottom, as a charm to safeguard the cattle against galling, and, secondly, never take the blossom indoors:

"Hawthorn blooms and Elder flowers
Fill the house with evil powers."

Despite this, our ancestors used Elder flowers extensively, for medicines, cosmetics, food and drink.

HAWTHORN (Crataegus monogyna) will lead the reader into a far reaching world of fact and fiction. It has been one of the supreme spiritual trees of our ancestors and all the more interesting for its mythology coming to us from France whereas that of Rowan etc. is primarily Teutonic.

Attention has been paid to the Midsummer 'Herbs of St. John' but with Hawthorn the emphasis shifts to May Day. The month of May was known to the Saxons as thrimilci - the month when the cows were milked thrice - something that is now restricted to a few corners of Scotland. Just as that name has changed, so too the name of the tree has become May.

The exact connection between the tree, the month and dairying is not understood properly, which is surprising considering the great importance our ancestors placed upon this. Dairying is the only agricultural activity to be closely involved with the Hawthorn, although its fertility rites were performed by fruit growers.

The association began at birth. In some regions, such as Cleveland, stockmen placed the afterbirth upon thorn trees so that the power of the tree would be transferred (by sympathetic magic) to the new calf. The cattle were kept, if possible, in a field with a lone thorn tree, for around it, under it and in it lived the fairies; the Fairy Queen herself according to my mother as she thrashed me with the branch I had broken off. One does not pick pieces of the Queen's home; she will not like it. Tracing back the myths to early forms leads to the interpretation that the Queen of the May tree was the great Mother goddess. Her apparent vindictiveness is really her maternal protection. Thus when treated respectfully the power of the tree ensured safety and also brought fertility. Thus branches were hung outside cowsheds to ensure a good milk yield. Yes, they could be picked but not brought into the home, except as part of the May Day rituals. On that day the powers were invoked against witches and all evil, which were also celebrating the arrival of summer. In particular the Hawthorn safeguarded farm produce but it is milk and butter which are singled out in the folklore.

Butter roller.
Thought to be for making Irish
butter brought in to Liverpool.

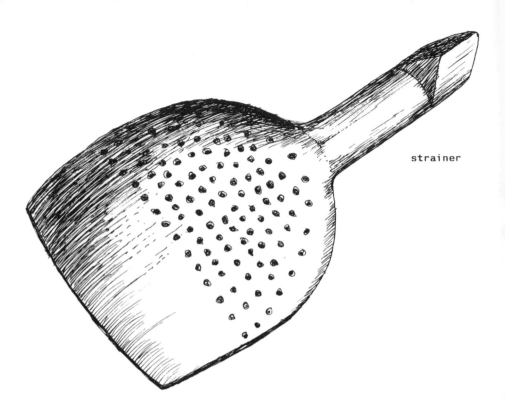

strainer

WAYFARING TREE (Viburnum lantana) was "planted around cattle stalls to ward off betwitchment" observed John Evelyn in the 17th century. Whether by 'planted' he means just that or is using the word in the sense 'positioned' or nailed up, isn't clear. Little folklore concerning this tree and dairying has been traced for this study, this is due in part to the tree being native only in the southern half of the country. It would have been, and still is, common on the chalk around Evelyn's Surrey estates. On the Wiltshire and Buckinghamshire chalk it has been known as Coven-tree, presumably preserving its associations with witches. In the more southern counties its names record the practice of twisting its pliant stems into whips (Twistwood in Hampshire; Whipcrop on the Isle of Wight; Whiptop in Dorset) which again suggests drovers used it in similar ways to those listed above for Rowan. Entwining the stems increased the magic powers, as in those beautiful May Day garlands etc. Another example is to entwine and bind with red thread, twigs of Oak, Ash and Hawthorn as a charm against evil.

Lastly, stirring the milk caused great concern. Evil might be stirred in at the same time and there was fear of doing that in all manner of culinary activities, from folding the Devil into the bread dough, to poking him into the meat with a skewer.

It must be said that cooks did not blame all their failures on the Devil - when milk wouldn't curdle a practical explanation was sought. Sometimes, they realised, it was due to the cows feeding on **WOOD SORREL**, Oxalis acetosella. Nevertheless something rather potent was needed as a milk stirrer and the chosen wood came from the Celtic Tree of Knowledge, the Hazel.

HAZEL (Corylus avellana) would surely 'know' how to keep the evil out. Apart from that, it had its own protector, Hynde Etin, whose particular strength was in defending the unripe nuts. At a Surrey fruit farm in the late 1950s the children were still being frightened from stealing fruit on Sundays, when there was nobody on duty, by warnings of the big brown hairy hand that would come out of the nut trees and throttle them. Related to Hynde Etin were the Boggarts who were the good Brownies who had been offended and turned nasty. These were known as Churn Milk Peg in Yorkshire but there are innumerable local names and beliefs.

Although the Hazel has the greatest tradition,(or Rowan where Hazel doesn't grow), one of the collectors whose dairying items were drawn for the illustration in this book, had been informed by a knowledgeable old farmer that stirrers were made of **CHERRY** (Prunus spp. and hybrids). An example has been sought ever since but in vain. No justification in the folklore of the **GEAN** (Prunus avium) has been found so far. Can any reader help? Perhaps this arises from the period when Cherry wood was in demand for high class furniture and even mundane items like milk stirrers were only considered top quality if made from the wood.

INDEX

Fagus sylvatica	58,76,77.
Fat-hen	42.
Fennel	28,30,31,82.
Ficus	54,69.
Fig	54,69.
Foeniculum vulgare	28,30,31,82.
Foxglove	40.
Fraxinus excelsior	41,48,50,51,85,92.
Galega	28.
Galega officinalis ·	32,69.
Galium aparine	67.
Galium verum	69,70.
Garlic	74.
Gean	93.
Goat's Rue	32,69.
Goosegrass	67.
Grass	46.
Gratiola officinalis	33.
Hazel	47,51,86,93.
Heather	49.
Hedera helix	39,85.
Hedge Hyssop	33.
Hemp	46.
Holly	57,58,61.
Hornbeam	50.
Horsetail	49.
Hyacinthoides non-scripta	40.
Hypericum perforatum	82,83.
Ilex aquifolium	57,58,61.
Ivy	39,85.
Lapsana communis	69.
Leek	74.
Lime	50.
Madder	69.
Malus spp.	60.
Mandragora officinalis	42.
Mandrake	42.
Mentha arvensis	44,45.
Mentha spicata	44,45.
Milkwort, Bitter	33.
Milkwort, Common	33.
Nettles, Stinging	36,37,49,70,72.
Nipplewort	69.

Oak	39,48,78,79,92.
Onion	74.
Oxalis acetosella	93.
Papaver rhoeas	43.
Petasites hybridus	62,63.
Pimpinella anisum	28,29.
Pimpinella saxifraga	28,33.
Polygala amara	33.
Polygala vulgaris	28,33.
Poppy, Corn	43.
Prunus spp.	93.
Pteridium aquilinum	40,70.
Quercus spp.	39,48,78,79,92.
Ranunculus	34.
Ranunculus scleratus	34.
Rowan	86,87,88.
Rubia spp.	69.
Saffron	69.
Sage	74.
St. John's Wort	82,83.
Salix spp.	47.
Salivia officinalis	74.
Sambucus nigra	46,88,89,90.
Sorbus aucuparia	86,87,88.
Spearmint	44,45.
Sycamore	49,53,54,55,79.
Taraxacum officinale	34.
Teasel	72.
Thistle	69.
Thistle, Carline	71.
Tilia spp.	50.
Tussilago farfara	62,64.
Ulmus spp.	58,77,78,79,80,81,85.
Urtica dioica	36,37,49,70,72.
Viburnum lantana	92.
Wayfaring tree	92.
Willow	47.
Wood sorrel	93.

* *

FOR LISTS OF OTHER PUBLICATIONS AND TALKS FOR GROUPS,
Write to:
Mr C Howkins, 70 Grange Rd, New Haw, Surrey. KT15 3RH